Make it easy...

Maths

Age 5-6

Paul Broadbent

Numbers to *10*

Look at these numbers and say them out loud.

zero one two three four five six seven eight nine ten

I Draw over the numbers. Join each one to its matching picture.

1 2 3 4 5 6 7 8 9 10

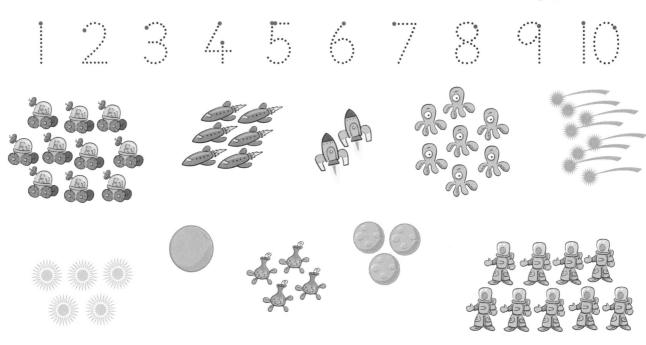

II Write the number on each planet to match each word.

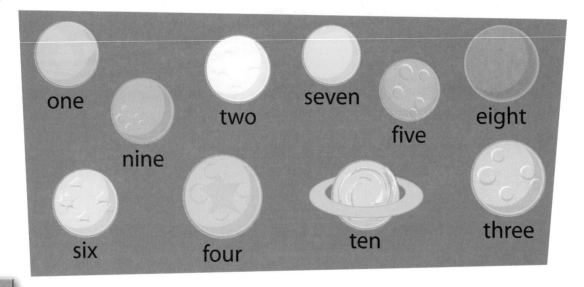

one two seven eight five nine six four ten three

Counting

Count the shells and say the numbers out loud.

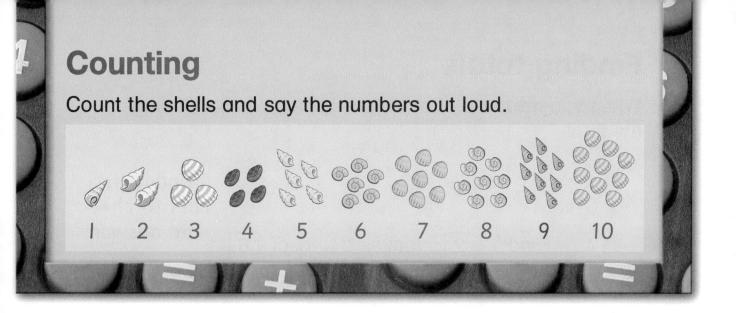

I Count the things in each group. Write the number.

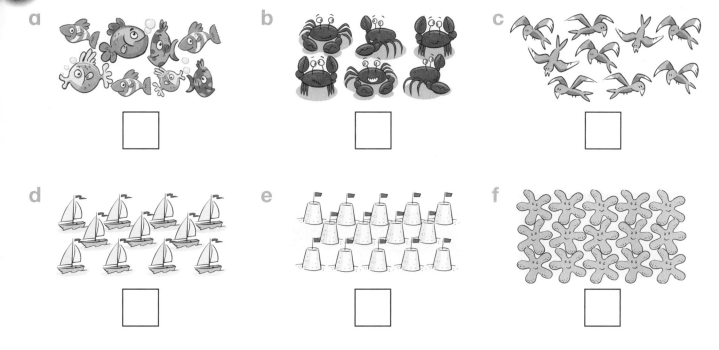

a

b

c

d

e

f

II Draw 10 more fish in the pool.

There are ☐ fish altogether.

Finding totals

When you **add** sets of objects together, you are finding the total.

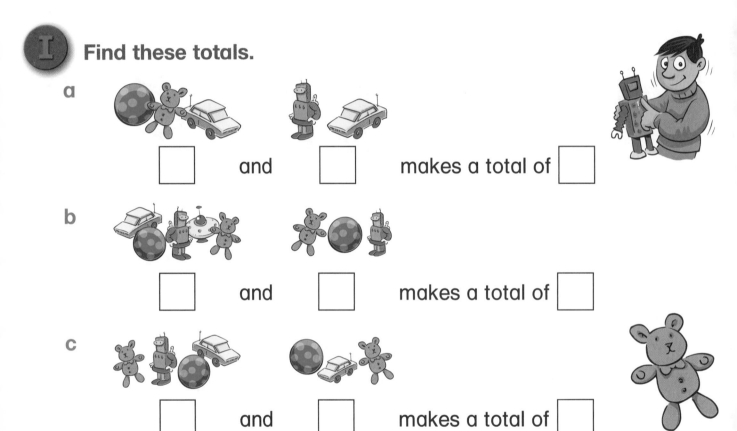

4 and 2 makes a total of 6

Count the cars to check the answer.

I Find these totals.

a

☐ and ☐ makes a total of ☐

b

☐ and ☐ makes a total of ☐

c

☐ and ☐ makes a total of ☐

II Draw extra beans so each set makes a total of 8.

8

2-D shapes

Look around you for these 2-D shapes. Try to remember their names.

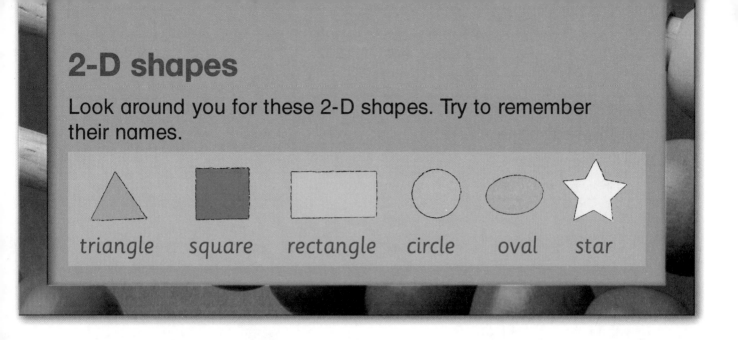

triangle   square   rectangle   circle   oval   star

I Colour the shapes to match the code. Count the number of each shape.

Number of shapes

II Draw lines to join each shape to its name.

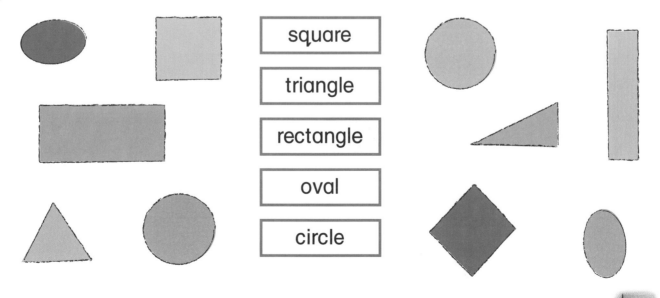

square

triangle

rectangle

oval

circle

5

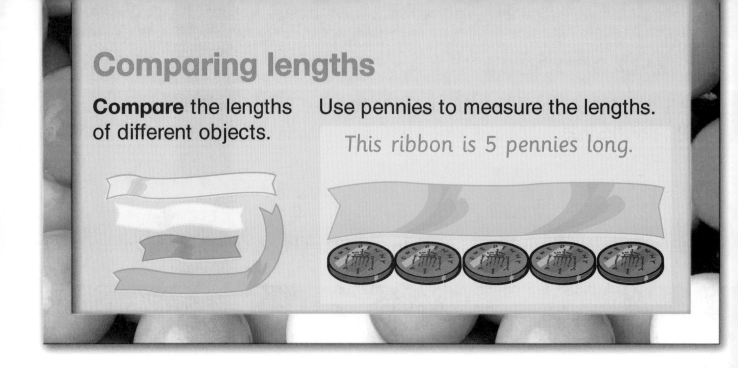

Comparing lengths

Compare the lengths of different objects.

Use pennies to measure the lengths.

This ribbon is 5 pennies long.

I Look at these objects.

a Circle the longest in each group.

b Circle the shortest in each group.

II Measure these lines using pennies.

a [ ] pennies

b [ ] pennies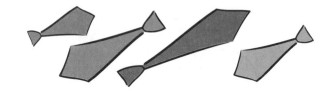

c [ ] pennies

d [ ] pennies

e [ ] pennies

6

O'clock time

When the long minute hand points to 12, it is an **o'clock time**.

On a digital clock, an o'clock time ends with **00**.

This is 4 o'clock.

I Write the time shown on each clock.

a

☐ o'clock

b

☐ o'clock

c

☐ o'clock

d

☐ o'clock

e

☐ o'clock

f

☐ o'clock

g

☐ o'clock

h

☐ o'clock

II Here are some activities Jack does each Saturday. Show the time he finishes each of them.

a

start ➜ 1 hour ➜ finish

b

start ➜ 3 hours ➜ finish

c

start ➜ 2 hours ➜ finish

d

start ➜ 1 hour ➜ finish

Numbers to 20

Look at these numbers and say them out loud.

11 eleven	14 fourteen	17 seventeen	20 twenty
12 twelve	15 fifteen	18 eighteen	
13 thirteen	16 sixteen	19 nineteen	

I Draw over each number, starting at the red dot.

11   12   16   17

14   13   18   19

15   20

II Write the number to match each word.

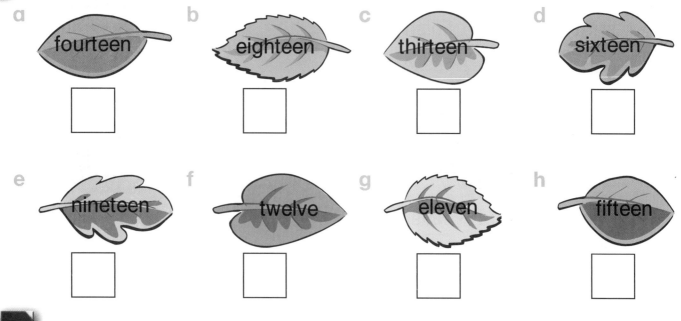

a fourteen ☐
b eighteen ☐
c thirteen ☐
d sixteen ☐

e nineteen ☐
f twelve ☐
g eleven ☐
h fifteen ☐

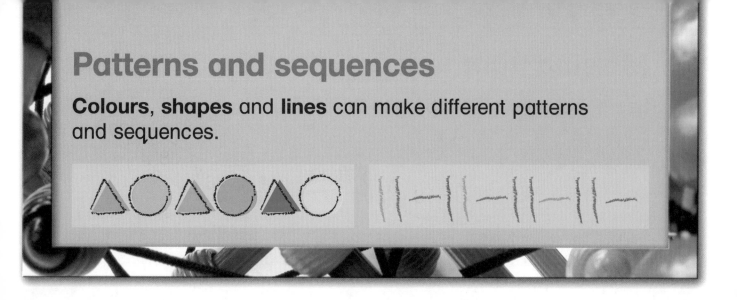

Patterns and sequences

Colours, **shapes** and **lines** can make different patterns and sequences.

I Continue drawing each pattern.

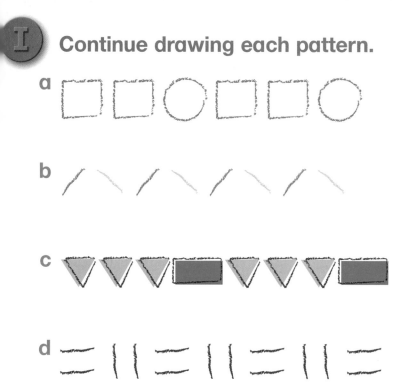

a

b

c

d

II Draw over these. Colour to make a pattern.

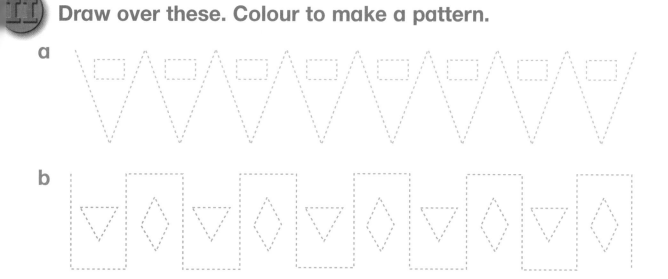

a

b

9

Missing numbers

Learn the order of numbers to **20**.

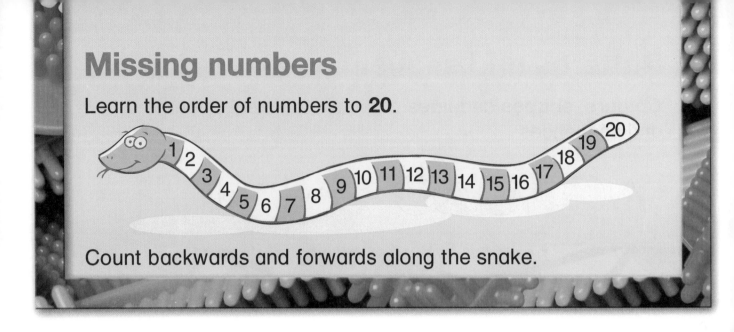

Count backwards and forwards along the snake.

I Write the missing numbers.

a 7 8   11   14

b   15 16 17   20

c 18 17 16   13

d   10 9   5 4

II Write these numbers as words. What is the hidden, shaded number?

12	→
15	→
18	→
13	→
10	→

The shaded number is ☐ .

Counting forwards and backwards

Practise counting **forwards** and **backwards** on a number line.

Follow the jumps with your finger.

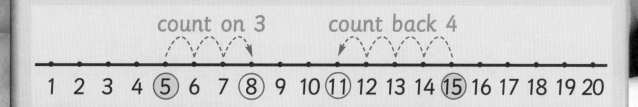

I   **Write the answers. Use the number line above to help.**

a   3 → Count on 2 → ☐   e   ☐ ← Count back 2 ← 8

b   7 → Count on 3 → ☐   f   ☐ ← Count back 4 ← 12

c   11 → Count on 5 → ☐   g   ☐ ← Count back 3 ← 16

d   10 → Count on 4 → ☐   h   ☐ ← Count back 5 ← 14

II   **Draw the jumps to show the counting on or back. Circle the number you finish on.**

a Count on 4

c Count back 2

b Count on 3

d Count back 5

Starting to add

We use the **+** sign to show **adding**.

= is the **equals** sign.

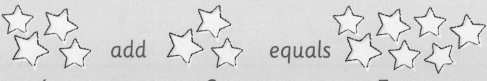

4   +   3   =   7

I   **Write the numbers for these additions.**

a

☐ + ☐ = ☐

c

☐ + ☐ = ☐

b

☐ + ☐ = ☐

d

☐ + ☐ = ☐

II   **Draw some more spots to help work out the missing numbers.**

a

3   +   ☐   = 7

c

4   +   ☐   = 6

b

2   +   ☐   = 5

d

5   +   ☐   = 9

3-D shapes

Look around you for these 3-D shapes. Try to remember their names.

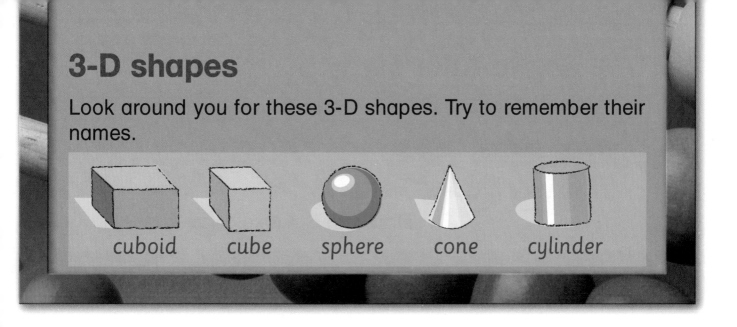

cuboid   cube   sphere   cone   cylinder

I   **Draw lines to join each shape to its name.**

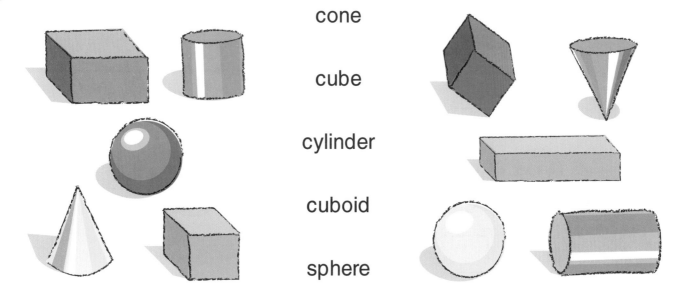

cone

cube

cylinder

cuboid

sphere

II   **Colour in the shapes that have all flat faces.**

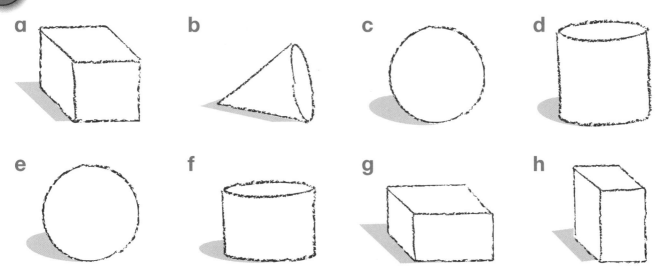

a   b   c   d

e   f   g   h

Starting to take away

We use the − sign when we **subtract** or **take away**.

$$5 - 2 = 3$$

start with 5   take away 2   3 left

I Cross out some buns to help answer these.

a

5 − 4 = ☐

c

4 − 2 = ☐

b
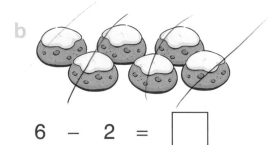

6 − 2 = ☐

d
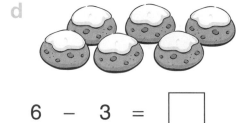

6 − 3 = ☐

II Write out a subtraction for each of these.

a

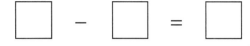

☐ − ☐ = ☐

c

☐ − ☐ = ☐

b

☐ − ☐ = ☐

d

☐ − ☐ = ☐

Recognising coins

Try to learn these **coins**.

| 1p | 2p | 5p | 10p | 20p | 50p |

I Cross out the odd one in each set.

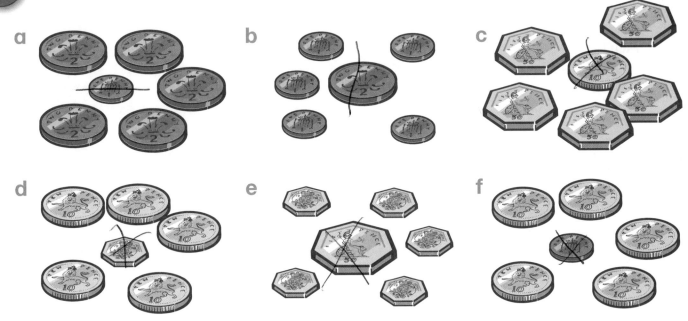

a

b

c

d

e

f

II Write the totals for each of these.

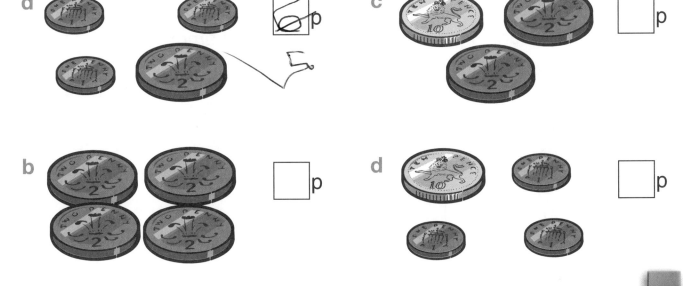

a ☐p

b ☐p

c ☐p

d ☐p

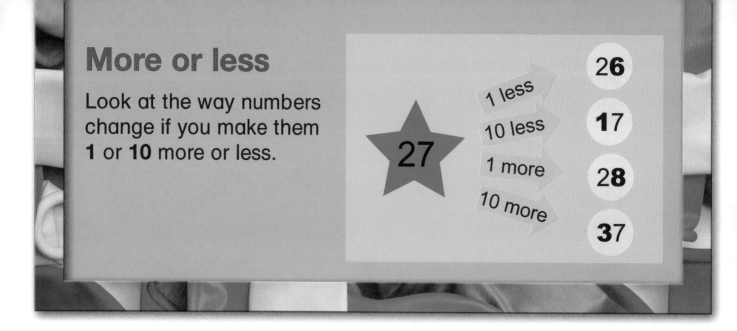

More or less

Look at the way numbers change if you make them **1** or **10** more or less.

27

1 less — 26
10 less — 17
1 more — 28
10 more — 37

 **Answer these.**

a Add 1 more.

13 → ◇   18 → ✦

26 → ○   31 → □

b Make 1 less.

19 → ◇   15 → ✦

26 → ○   20 → □

c Add 10 more.

7 → ◇   19 → ✦

14 → ○   22 → □

d Make 10 less.

18 → ◇   21 → ✦

32 → ○   29 → □

Count how much money is in each purse.

a Add 1p and write the total amount.

☐ p   ☐ p

b Add 10p and write the total amount.

☐ p   ☐ p

Odds and evens

Say these odd and even numbers out loud.

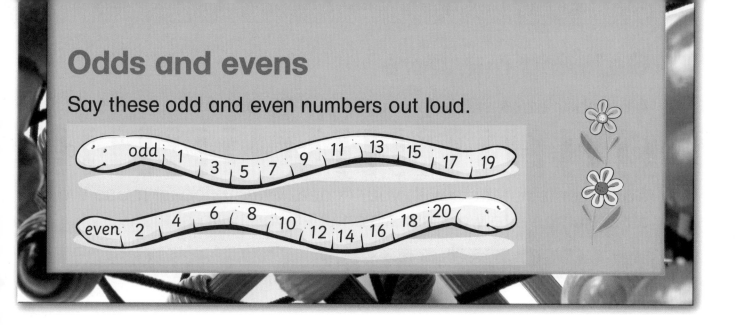

I **Try to do these odd and even problems.**

a Tick the shields with an even number of dots.

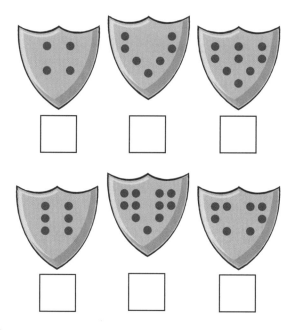

b Colour all the badges with even numbers.

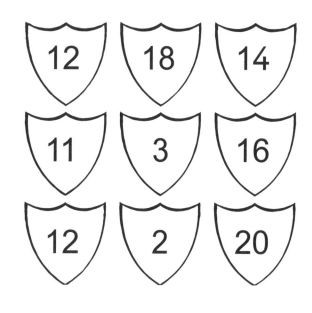

II **Now try these problems.**

a Write the next odd numbers.

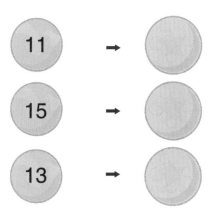

11 →

15 →

13 →

b Write the next even numbers.

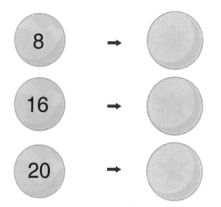

8 →

16 →

20 →

Ordering numbers

A **number track** will help you to learn the order of numbers.

0 1 2 3 4 5 6 7 8 9 10 11 12 13 14 15 16 17 18 19 20

Cover some numbers with your fingers without looking. Use the other numbers to work out which ones you have hidden.

I These numbers have fallen off the washing on each line. Put them back in the correct order.

a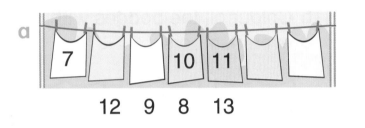

12   9   8   13

c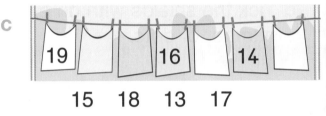

15   18   13   17

b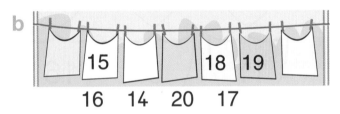

16   14   20   17

d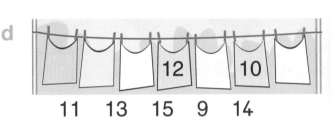

11   13   15   9   14

II Draw lines to join the price labels to the correct tins. The prices should be in order.

Lowest ⟶ Highest

Teen numbers

Teen numbers are made from a **10** and some **1s**.

Read these numbers aloud.

13	14	15	16	17	18	19
10+3	10+4	10+5	10+6	10+7	10+8	10+9

11 and 12 are also made from a 10 and some 1s.

I Write the missing numbers.

a fifteen → $\boxed{10}$ + $\square$ f twelve → $\square$ + $\square$

b eighteen → $\square$ + $\square$ g fourteen → $\square$ + $\square$

c eleven → $\square$ + $\square$ h thirteen → $\square$ + $\square$

d sixteen → $\square$ + $\square$ i seventeen → $\square$ + $\square$

e nineteen → $\square$ + $\square$ j twenty → $\square$ + $\square$

II Write these answers in words.

a 10 + 3 →   e 10 + 2 →

b 10 + 1 →   f 10 + 6 →

c 10 + 9 →   g 10 + 7 →

d 10 + 4 →   h 10 + 8 →

Comparing numbers

When you compare numbers you can use a number line to work out which number is bigger and which is smaller.

12   13   14   15   16

15 is bigger than 12.

I Look at these pairs of numbers.

a Colour the bigger number red.

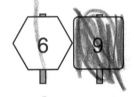

6   9   14   7

13   14   18   20

21   19   25   22

b Colour the smaller number blue.

11   7   9   13

18   19   14   10

21   23   18   25

II Write the missing numbers between these pairs of numbers.

a
6   9

b
11   14

c
17   20

d
12   15

e
19   22

f
23   26

Ordinal numbers

1st, 2nd, 3rd … are called ordinal numbers.

They show the **order of things**.

first	second	third	fourth	fifth	sixth	seventh	eighth
1st	2nd	3rd	4th	5th	6th	7th	8th

 Look at the order of the letters in the alphabet.

A B C D E F G H I J K L M N O P Q R S T U V W X Y Z

Complete these.

The 1st letter is ☐.   F is the ☐ letter.

The 5th letter is ☐.   C is the ☐ letter.

The 7th letter is ☐.   L is the ☐ letter.

The 4th letter is ☐.   P is the ☐ letter.

The last letter is ☐.   B is the ☐ letter.

 Use the alphabet order to work out these word puzzles.

a   13th   1st   20th   8th   19th

☐M☐   ☐   ☐   ☐   ☐

b   13th   1st   7th   9th   3rd

☐M☐   ☐   ☐   ☐   ☐

Now try making up your own puzzles.

Days of the week

Try to learn the **order** of the days of the week.

 How well have you learnt the days of the week?

a Draw lines to join each day to the one that follows it.

b Now join each day to the one that comes before it.

Friday
Wednesday
Monday
Sunday
Tuesday
Thursday   Saturday

Saturday
Monday
Thursday
Friday
Sunday
Tuesday   Wednesday

 Fill in the gaps to show what day it is.

W e __ __ __ __ d a y

S __ __ u r __ __ y

F __ __ __ a y

__ o n d __ __

S u __ __ a y

__ __ u r s d __ __

T __ e __ d __ y

MONDAY
TUESDAY
WEDNESDAY
THURSDAY
FRIDAY
SATURDAY
SUNDAY

Money

You need to know what these **coins** are worth.

1p 2p 5p 10p 20p 50p

p means pence. There are 50 pence or pennies in 50p.

I Add up the value of these coins to find the total.

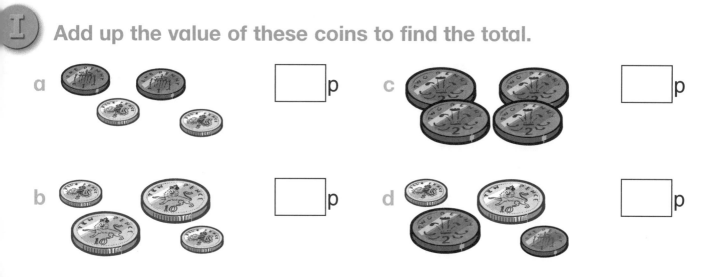

a [ ]p

c [ ]p

b [ ]p

d [ ]p

II Draw the coins you would use to buy these sweets.

a   7p

b   16p

c   11p

Adding

Use a **number track** like this to help you add.

$$2 + 3 = 5$$

+3

0 1 2 3 4 5 6 7 8 9 10

I Use the number track to help you add these.

a 3 + 4 = ☐   f 2 + 5 = ☐   k 4 + 5 = ☐

b 1 + 3 = ☐   g 4 + 4 = ☐   l 6 + 3 = ☐

c 4 + 2 = ☐   h 3 + 2 = ☐   m 5 + 1 = ☐

d 0 + 2 = ☐   i 0 + 5 = ☐   n 8 + 2 = ☐

e 3 + 3 = ☐   j 5 + 3 = ☐   o 3 + 7 = ☐

II Write the numbers coming out of the machines.

a 3   ☐   e 2   ☐

b 5   ☐   f 5   ☐

c 2   ☐   g 4   ☐

d 6   ☐   h 1   ☐

Taking away

You can count back along a number line to help you **subtract** or **take away**.

$$8 - 3 = 5$$

4   5   6   7   8   9   10

I Use the number lines to help you complete these.

a

5   6   7   8   9   10

$9 - 4 = \boxed{}$

b

1   2   3   4   5   6   7

$7 - \boxed{} = 3$

c

2   3   4   5   6   7   8

$8 - \boxed{} = 4$

d
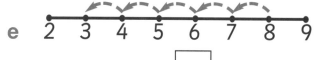

5   6   7   8   9   10

$10 - \boxed{} = 7$

e

2   3   4   5   6   7   8   9

$8 - 5 = \boxed{}$

f

1   2   3   4   5   6   7

$5 - \boxed{} = 3$

II Colour the tyre which gives a different answer to the others in the pile.

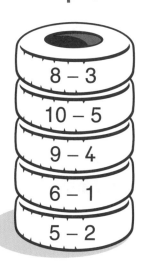

a
- 8 – 3
- 10 – 5
- 9 – 4
- 6 – 1
- 5 – 2

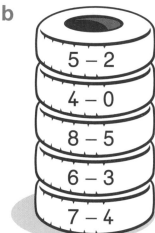

b
- 5 – 2
- 4 – 0
- 8 – 5
- 6 – 3
- 7 – 4

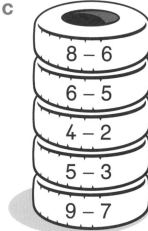

c
- 8 – 6
- 6 – 5
- 4 – 2
- 5 – 3
- 9 – 7

Measuring

Mass and capacity are 2 ways of measuring.

Mass

We use the words *heavy* and *light* when talking about mass, or weight.

Capacity

The capacity is how much something holds.

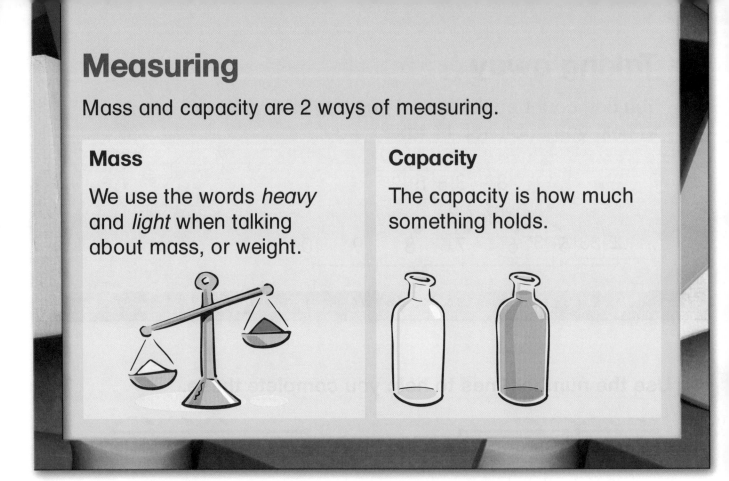

I Which objects are heavy and which are light? Circle the lightest ones.

a
b
c

II Look at these containers. Draw lines to join them in order. Start with the smallest capacity.

Counting patterns

Use this number grid to help you with **counting patterns**.

1	2	3	4	5	6	7	8	9	10
11	12	13	14	15	16	17	18	19	20
21	22	23	24	25	26	27	28	29	30
31	32	33	34	35	36	37	38	39	40

I **Look at the numbers on the track.**

Colour the number 2 red.

Miss out number 3 and colour number 4 red.

Miss out number 5 and colour number 6 red.

Continue colouring this pattern.

1	2	3	4	5	6	7	8	9	10	11	12	13	14	15	16	17	18	19	20

a The red numbers are called _____ numbers.

b The other numbers are called _____ numbers.

II **Continue these counting patterns.**

a 20 19 18 17

b 4 6 8 10

c 9 11 13 15

d 5 10 15 20

e 30 28 26 24

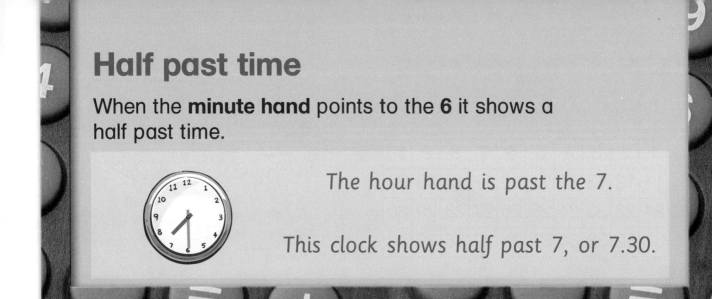

Half past time

When the **minute hand** points to the **6** it shows a half past time.

The hour hand is past the 7.

This clock shows half past 7, or 7.30.

I Write out these times in the boxes.

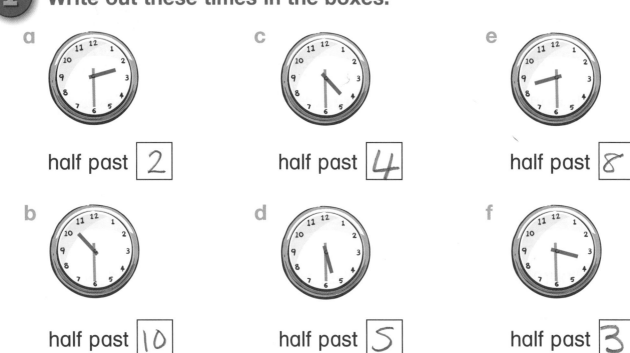

a
half past 2

c
half past 4

e
half past 8

b
half past 10

d
half past 5

f
half past 3

II Draw lines to join the clocks that show the same time.

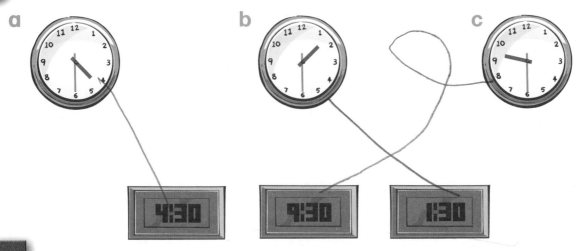

a

b

c

4:30   9:30   1:30

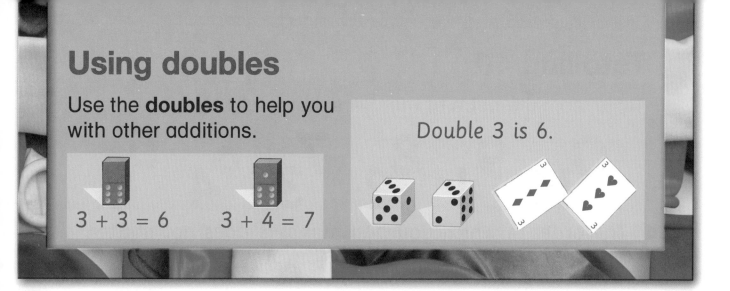

Using doubles

Use the **doubles** to help you with other additions.

$3 + 3 = 6$ $3 + 4 = 7$

Double 3 is 6.

I Write the answers in the boxes.

a  $3 + 3 = \boxed{}$

b $2 + 2 = \boxed{}$

c $5 + 5 = \boxed{}$

d $4 + 4 = \boxed{}$

e $1 + 1 = \boxed{}$

f  $2 + 3 = \boxed{}$

g  $4 + 5 = \boxed{}$

h  $1 + 2 = \boxed{}$

i  $3 + 4 = \boxed{}$

j  $5 + 6 = \boxed{}$

II Draw more dots on each domino to match the total in the box below.

a

b

c

d

e

| 9 | 7 | 5 | 11 | 12 |

Totalling 10

Try to learn the **pairs of numbers** that total 10.

$$0_{10} \quad 9_1 \quad 8_2 \quad 7_3 \quad 6_4 \quad 5_5$$

The order in which you add numbers does not matter.
$8 + 2$ and $2 + 8$ both total 10.

I Write the missing numbers.

a $3 + \boxed{} = 10$ e $\boxed{} + 0 = 10$ i $1 + \boxed{} = 10$

b $8 + \boxed{} = 10$ f $\boxed{} + 9 = 10$ j $\boxed{} + 4 = 10$

c $4 + \boxed{} = 10$ g $\boxed{} + 8 = 10$ k $10 + \boxed{} = 10$

d $5 + \boxed{} = 10$ h $\boxed{} + 7 = 10$ l $\boxed{} + 5 = 10$

II Corner numbers add up to 10. Write the missing corner numbers for each of these.

a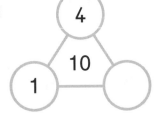

c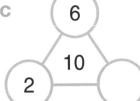

e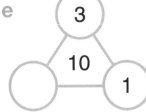

b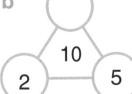

d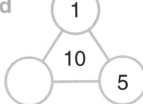

Finding the difference

A **number track** is very useful for finding the difference between 2 numbers.

Count on from 4 to 7, counting the jumps.

The difference between 4 and 7 is 3.

I Draw the jumps to find the difference between these pairs of numbers in **red**.

a

The difference is ☐.

c

The difference is ☐.

b

The difference is ☐.

d

The difference is ☐.

II Draw lines to join the pairs of numbers with a difference of 4.

ANSWERS

Page 2
I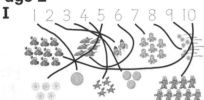

1 2 3 4 5 6 7 8 9 10

II one → 1   six → 6
two → 2   seven → 7
three → 3   eight → 8
four → 4   nine → 9
five → 5   ten → 10

Page 3
I **a** 8   **b** 6   **c** 9
d 11   **e** 14   **f** 15

II There are 20 fish altogether.

Page 4
I **a** 3 and 2 makes a total of 5
b 5 and 3 makes a total of 8
c 4 and 3 makes a total of 7

II Check there are now 8 beans in each set.

Page 5
I

△	5	●	5
■	6	⬭	2
▭	1

II

square
triangle
rectangle
oval
circle

Page 6
I **a**

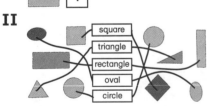

b

II **a** 3 pennies
b 5 pennies
c 2 pennies
d 4 pennies
e 3 pennies

Page 7
I **a** 7 o'clock
b 1 o'clock
c 6 o'clock
d 8 o'clock
e 9 o'clock
f 3 o'clock
g 11 o'clock
h 10 o'clock

II **a**   **c**

b   **d**

Page 8
I Check child's writing.

II **a** 14   **b** 18   **c** 13
d 16   **e** 19   **f** 12
g 11   **h** 15

Page 9
I Check child's patterns.

II Check child's patterns.

Page 10
I **a** 7, 8, 9, 10, 11, 12, 13, 14, 15, 16
b 11, 12, 13, 14, 15, 16, 17, 18, 19, 20
c 18, 17, 16, 15, 14, 13, 12, 11, 10, 9
d 12, 11, 10, 9, 8, 7, 6, 5, 4, 3

II

t	w	e	l	v	e
	f	i	f	t	e	e	n
e	i	g	h	t	e	e	n
t	h	i	r	t	e	e	n
	t	e	n

The shaded number is 8.

Page 11
I **a** 5   **d** 14   **g** 13
b 10   **e** 6   **h** 9
c 16   **f** 8

II **a** 3 4 5 6 ⑦ 8 9
b 5 6 7 8 ⑨ 10 11
c 2 3 4 ⑤ 6 7 8
d 6 ⑦ 8 9 10 11 12

Page 12
I **a** 3 + 2 = 5   **c** 4 + 4 = 8
b 3 + 3 = 6   **d** 5 + 3 = 8

II **a** 4   **c** 2
b 3   **d** 4

Page 13
I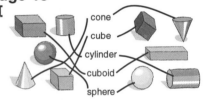

cone
cube
cylinder
cuboid
sphere

II Check child has coloured a, g and h.

Page 14
I Check child has crossed out correct number of buns.
a 1   **c** 2
b 4   **d** 3

II **a** 6 − 4 = 2   **c** 5 − 3 = 2
b 7 − 3 = 4   **d** 6 − 5 = 1

Page 15
I Check these coins have been crossed out.
a 1p   **d** 20p
b 2p   **e** 50p
c 10p   **f** 1p